P R I

Disease

MATT RIDLEY

PHŒNIX

A PHOENIX PAPERBACK

First published in Great Britain in 1997 by
Phoenix, a division of the Orion Publishing Group Ltd
Orion House
5 Upper Saint Martin's Lane
London, WC2H 9EA

A CIP catalogue record for this book is available
from the British Library.

ISBN 0 297 84065 7

Typeset by SetSystems Ltd, Saffron Walden
Set in 9/13.5 Stone Serif
Printed in Great Britain by
Clays Ltd, St Ives plc

Contents

Chapter 1
A Tale of Two Viruses

In 1972, a woman – we'll call her by her medical name, Patient 3 – left her home in the district of Yambuku in central Zaire and made the long journey to the city of Kinshasa. She lived there as a *femme libre* for four years, making ends meet by prostitution. In 1976 she returned to Yambuku at the age of thirty-six. Shortly after her arrival, but through no fault of hers, the place became a vision of hell. Inexplicably and suddenly people began to die. They did not die peacefully; they disintegrated. One day they felt aches in their joints and a sore throat. Three days of feverish, delirious vomiting later, covered in skin pustules, bleeding from nose, mouth and rectum, they went into fatal shock. Within a month, forty people had died in Patient 3's village – a place of just 300 souls. They were the first recorded victims of possibly the most deadly strain of virus ever discovered: Ebola Zaire.

But Patient 3 did not die of Ebola virus. Perhaps she stayed away from the mission hospital where most victims caught the disease, from hypodermic needles used and reused by the well-meaning nuns of the Soeurs du Saint Coeur Marie. Perhaps she had no close relatives to bury so she did not evacuate the bowels of a corpse by hand in the traditional pre-funereal ritual. Certainly she was alive when Belgian and American doctors flew into the area in search of clues to the cause of the outbreak; they took a blood sample from her.

Or perhaps she was already unwell for a different reason. A few months after the Ebola plague, as she counted her luck at having survived it, she began to suffer from diarrhoea. She could not shake off her cough. She frequently felt feverish. She began to lose weight. Her health went from bad to terrible. By the middle of the next year, she was dead. She is buried in Yambuku beneath a simple gravestone. The blood sample, held in a freezer in Atlanta, Georgia, holds a clue to her premature death. In 1976 she was HIV-positive. Her sample is the oldest blood sample in the world with the AIDS virus in it.

Where she contracted HIV remains a mystery, but she did so many years before it was known to science and a decade before people began to die of AIDS all across Central Africa. She was not alone: four other people in the Yambuku area carried antibodies to the virus at the same time; three are dead. Chances are, HIV was a rare but ancient infection of people in the basin of the Congo river. Patient 3 may even have been the first person to carry it to the brothels of Kinshasa, whence it spread to so much of the rest of the world. More likely, somebody had already carried it there and she brought it back east into the forest. Whatever the truth, Patient 3 dodged one plague new to the human race, but not a second. The rest of humankind would soon do the same. In the twenty-one years since then, Ebola virus has turned out to be a paper tiger, incapable of sustaining a major epidemic for long – too lethal for its own good.

HIV, far less easy to catch but much better at keeping

its victims healthy enough to infect others, is rapidly joining the great plagues of history. It is less contagious than bubonic plague, smallpox or measles. It spreads more slowly than influenza or cholera. It kills more gradually than typhus or yellow fever. But like those diseases in their heydays it is global, frequently fatal and cruelly hard to cure. In 1976 the medical world was celebrating the imminent extinction of smallpox, which would officially happen a year later with the recovery of Ali Maow Maalin in Somalia – the last man to catch the disease in the wild. Yet all we had achieved was to swap one plague for another. We enter the third millennium with as many dangerous parasites on board as ever.

The conventional wisdom about infectious disease has swung from one extreme to another. From the hubristic optimism of the 1960s, when the United States Surgeon-General said we could 'close the book on infectious disease', we have plunged into alarmism. Publishers and film producers have reopened the book with lucrative results. *The Hot Zone*, *Outbreak*, *Plagues*, *Virus X*, *The Coming Plague*, *Plagues and Progress*, *The Virus Hunters*: the titles of recent books screech their pessimism. All argue, to a greater or lesser extent, that we are doomed unless we take urgent action. Infectious death is on the way back into our lives, part of the planet's ecological revenge for our despoliation of it. It has happened to other successful species. Irish potato blight altered world history. Dutch elm disease spared hardly an elm tree in Britain. Myxomatosis killed 99 per cent of southern Australia's rabbits in its first wave. Could it be our turn next?

This book makes two predictions in answer to that question. The first is that there is no end to the struggle with disease. Infection is never going to be entirely defeated, however well we organize our governments, however ingeniously we invent new cures and however much we stop interfering with nature. The ten or eleven billion people that will inhabit this globe at the peak of world population midway through the next century present too tempting a target to the microbial world, too gigantic an ecological niche to be left vacant. It is not in the nature of the war of attrition between a parasite and its host for either side to declare victory or accept defeat. There is no such thing as surrender.

Yet, second, much pessimism is misplaced. Some fatal, epidemic and chronic diseases will persist for ever. But most of the successful ones will be mild, like colds, or relatively hard to catch, like AIDS. And, far from living near the end of a brief golden age of drugs – after penicillin and before too many drug-resistant diseases – we are on the threshold of a new age of technology. DNA vaccines, molecular-designed drugs and genetically engineered resistance are only part of this. The other part is that played by ordinary technology. Our rat-free, mosquito-free, suburban houses, in which we live atomized, sanitized lives with purified water and little physical contact with strangers, offer handholds only to diseases that are among the mildest and most contagious. In other words, the common cold may get commoner, but mass epidemics of typhus, plague and Ebola virus are probably a thing of the past – for most of us at least. It is no accident that the common cold is actually an umbrella term covering more than 200 kinds of virus – rhinoviruses, coronaviruses, adenoviruses and others – yet none of them is life-threatening. Easy contagion and high virulence do not go together.

Chapter 2
Plagues of the Past

The plague came down the Nile from 'Ethiopia', according to Thucydides. From Egypt it spread to Libya and then appeared suddenly in Piraeus, the port of Athens, in 430BC. It soon reached Athens itself. In a single year, it killed a quarter of the Athenian army, shattered the morale of the city and in due course handed military supremacy to Sparta.

The plague of Athens is the first well-documented epidemic. It is probably futile to speculate about what it was, because, although the symptoms were well described by Thucydides, symptoms can change, especially when a disease first reaches a virgin population. It sounds, to modern ears, remarkably like Ebola virus: sore, red throat, aching and discomfort, skin pustules, retching and bleeding. If it came down the Nile as Thucydides said, maybe it was. One of the first known outbreaks of Ebola virus occurred in Sudan in 1976 on a tributary of the Nile. We will never know.

But from that date (or probably an earlier, unrecorded one – Egypt and Babylon were visited by frequent plagues, to judge by ancient texts), the human race became afflicted by a series of epidemic plagues, nearly all of which found their main opportunity to turn virulent in cities and armies. Some of these diseases, like Shigella dysentery, mumps, diphtheria and chicken pox, were simply old human pathogens that had taken the opportunity of denser human populations to turn virulent. Others may have recently jumped into the human species from their domesticated animals – measles from dogs and smallpox from cattle in India. Yet others were simply taking the opportunity to invade new areas where virgin immune systems awaited them.

Empires are good at spreading plagues because they send soldiers into distant lands and bring them back to mix in the empire's core. By the third century BC China was embarked on a history of sporadic plagues that continued until the present century. Empires also infected each other. In 162AD, a Chinese plague of unprecedented ferocity killed one-third of some armies fighting in the west of the empire. Just three years later, the Rome of Marcus Aurelius was devastated by a plague brought back by soldiers from the east. Outbreaks continued for fifteen years, weakening the empire and inviting barbarian invasions: in repulsing one of which, Marcus Aurelius himself died of the fever. This may have been the first appearance of measles in the Mediterranean. A century later in 251AD an even more vicious disease appeared, possibly smallpox. Rome was brought to its knees, never to recover its pre-eminence.

Constantinople's turn came in 542, at just the moment when Belisarius was on the brink of reuniting the Roman empire. This, the great plague of Justinian, announced the arrival in Europe, perhaps for the first time, of bubonic plague. According to one calculation, 48 per cent of the city's population died. Plague's main effect over the next two centuries was to shift the centre of civilization from the depopulated Mediterranean to Christendom and

Islamic Arabia. The plague reached China a century later, probably by sea.

For Europe, there then came a long pause. Disease continued to kill and disable during the Dark Ages and medieval period, but sudden and widespread epidemics seemed to peter out. Even during the Crusades, the worst mortality among besieging soldiers came from the non-infectious scurvy. The reason may be the feudal system, which encouraged a more even spread of the population, less trade and smaller cities. In China, too, there is a hint that the terrible plagues of the seventh century were not repeated with such intensity for 500 years. When an epidemic returned, it was not a new disease, but bubonic plague again.

Bubonic plague is a bacterial disease carried by fleas that will find a reservoir in any wild burrowing rodent. It is probably indigenous only in India, the original home of the black rat. But at some point it reached the rodents of the steppes of Central Asia and was delivered afresh by the Mongols to various parts of their empire. It reached Europe in 1346 aboard a ship from the Crimea, and found cities with thatched roofs teeming with black rats that dropped their fleas upon human backs. How many people died in this, the worst of all the epidemics? A third, says Froissart, half or more of those in some cities, say modern historians. A quarter even of rural peasants, say the demographers. Population continued to fall for nearly a century as waves of plague returned with diminishing severity.

As it recovered, Europe began to open up to the world, its trading and colonizing tentacles reaching around Africa to India and China, as well as across the Atlantic. This process brought Europeans three new epidemic diseases, one probably from America, one probably from Arabia and one probably from China. Syphilis, the virulent and sexually transmitted form of yaws, was almost certainly unknown in the Old World. To this day, despite frequent reports to the contrary, older skeletons showing syphilitic deformities have failed to appear on the eastern shore of the Atlantic, whereas they are common in the Americas. Syphilis reached Spain soon after Columbus' voyage, a coincidence too good to ignore, and by 1495 it was epidemic in a French army retreating from Naples. For nearly a century, the 'pox' would trouble Europe, ushering in a new religious abhorrence of sex.

Also making its European debut in Spain, and also playing its part in a siege of Naples (in 1528) was typhus, a louse-carried bacterium that would henceforth be the scourge of armies, jails and poor houses right into the twentieth century. Typhus probably came with the Moors from the Middle East, where it was known already; it first killed Europeans in 1489 in the wars between Spaniards and Arabs over the kingdom of Granada. If syphilis helped spark the religious purification that led to the Reformation, typhus took advantage of the religious wars that followed. In 1632 at Gustavus Adolphus' siege of Nuremberg, 29,000 of the besieged died in seven weeks while the typhus, showing no impartiality, forced the besiegers to retreat, leaving heaps of corpses behind them.

From China, meanwhile, came influenza, a strangely evanescent virus of wild ducks, new strains of which are still transmitted to man through domesticated Chinese ducks and pigs. Although it may have existed in Europe at an earlier date, the first great epidemic of influenza in Europe occurred in the 1550s. To this day new Chinese strains of influenza soon spread to Europe, though none has ever achieved the virulence of the strain that found its niche in the armies of the First World War.

But Europeans gave more than they got. In 1506, nine years after Vasco da Gama rounded the Cape of Good Hope, there was a devastating plague all across the Chinese empire. Was it some European speciality such as measles or smallpox? The Spaniards gave to the natives of America not only their home-grown scourges – smallpox reached Mexico in 1520, the year after Cortez, and measles in 1531 – but also their newly acquired ones: typhus in 1545 and influenza in the 1560s. The natives of the Americas, made vulnerable by their passage through a cold and narrow genetic bottleneck on the Bering isthmus 11,000 years before, were not only free of most diseases but were immunologically monotonous, which rendered them easy prey to the European germs. Germs adapt to the defences of their hosts; if an adaptation works in one individual, it will work in others that have similar genes. North, South and Central America suffered a population collapse unprecedented in history. Mexico's population shrank from twenty-five million to three million; Inca Peru's from eight million to one million. From being the most populous city in the world, Mexico City declined to a little town.

Meanwhile an old European disease, leprosy, was on the wane. Its decline, however, was probably caused by the resurgence of another, closely related disease, tuberculosis. Leprosy was probably originally a disease caught from water buffalo. Tuberculosis, like smallpox, jumped from cattle. They competed for the same niche, because immunity to one gives cross-immunity to the other. By the end of the Middle Ages, leprosy was almost extinct, but tuberculosis was rampant. It soon acquired an ability to infect human beings that would make it – even today – the most effective killer of all the infectious diseases. Every year it infects eight million new victims and takes maybe two million lives.

Tuberculosis thrived in post-medieval Europe for two principal reasons: the close proximity of strangers, in towns and cities, gave it the opportunity to spread; and the monotonous diet of the urban poor provided victims with weak immune systems in which the bacterium could get a beachhead. It was the archetypal symptom of the industrial age. When conditions began gradually to improve for the poor, tuberculosis began a long retreat – many decades before effective antibiotics became available. But its reappearance in multidrug-resistant form in recent years alongside AIDS and intravenous drug abuse is a symptom of how far we are from defeating it. The number of new cases diagnosed each year worldwide rose from seven and a half million in 1990 to nearly ten million in 1996.

The large cities of the industrial age gave an unprecedented opportunity to water-borne epidemic diseases, especially typhoid, dysentery and cholera. Cholera, as far as we can judge, was an endemic disease of the heavily populated Ganges delta until Calcutta became a large city under British rule. Then, quite suddenly in 1817, cholera consumed Calcutta, spread to other parts of Asia and thence to Arabia and East Africa, killing a large proportion of its many victims. In 1830, cholera reached Russia and Western Europe. Since it killed so many of its hosts and flushed itself so effectively from their bodies in diarrhoea, cholera was a disease that could sustain only brief epidemics in crowded cities where people drank water freely contaminated with sewage. As soon as sewers were separated from sources of drinking water, the pandemics of cholera ceased.

By 1960, infectious disease seemed to be on the retreat all over the world. Sanitation had defeated cholera, typhoid and dysentery. Hygiene had defeated typhus and bubonic plague. Better hospital practice had defeated scarlet fever. Nutrition was defeating tuberculosis. Vaccination was defeating smallpox and would soon defeat polio. DDT had defeated yellow fever and malaria. Antibiotics were defeating syphilis and gonorrhoea. There was no reason to be pessimistic about any germ in the world. According to the conventional wisdom of the age, the rising population of the world threatened a Malthusian crisis of starvation, not of disease.

Since then, there has been a retreat on almost all fronts. Cholera has achieved another epidemic, in Latin America. Bubonic plague broke out in India in the 1990s. Hospitals have encouraged the spread of hepatitis and drug-resistant staphylococcus. Tuberculosis is on the increase. Measles, rubella and whooping cough all mounted minor epidemics as vaccination rates began to fall. Smallpox is gone, thank goodness, and polio will be gone by 2000 (there were only about 100 cases last year), but other vaccines have failed to provide sufficient herd immunity to eradicate diseases. DDT has been defeated by resistant mosquitoes and by public alarm over the effects of the chemical on wildlife: malaria is back with a vengeance. Antibiotics are increasingly powerless in the face of drug-resistant strains of bacteria, including syphilis and gonorrhoea. And, to cap it all, a brand-new disease with high mortality has entered our species, thus far defeating all attempts to cure it or even to prevent its spread: AIDS.

Chapter 3
The Meaning of AIDS

If I had written this book before the AIDS epidemic, I would have been unflaggingly optimistic. The setbacks in the war against disease were no more than temporary retreats. Victory was still inevitable and the chance of a new disease threatening our species in the era of vaccines, antibiotics and public health measures was remote. But AIDS drives a coach and horses through such optimism. A virus appeared that killed people. We quickly recognized it, identified its method of attack, defined its biology, read its genes, deciphered the structure of its proteins and warned the world about it. We put our best brains on to defeating it. We made it a household word. All in vain. It spread through Africa and the Americas, crossed the seas to Europe and Asia and became so entrenched in our population that it is now the leading cause of death in young adults in many parts of the world. Twelve years after its first identification, there are some glimmers of hope: drugs that seemed to delay or reverse the onset of disease in those carrying the virus. But the fact remains that we have been well and truly humiliated by this little package of proteins and genes.

We may never know for sure where the human AIDS virus came from. Its closest relative is found not in monkeys, which carry a slightly different virus, but in apes: chimpanzees in particular. Chimps are ideally suited to carrying sexually transmitted diseases, because their social lives involve promiscuous sex among most members of each troop, and regular exchange of young females between troops. In them HIV seems to be only mildly harmful, which suggests that it may have been with them for ever. But it probably crossed the species barrier many times in the past. Blood samples preserved from various parts of Central Africa suggest that it was present at low levels during the 1970s in rural areas – indeed, at levels similar to its prevalence in such rural areas today. Like cholera in Bengal, or typhus before the siege of Naples, AIDS's opportunity came with a change in human habits.

Central Africa before the 1970s was a place where people rarely travelled far from their home towns. Held in traditional and nosy communities, HIV-infected people were very unlikely to infect more than one person before they died, so the virus could not spread outside small closed circles. But then transport routes opened up across the continent and with them came prostitution. All the evidence suggests that it was in the trucks, barges and armies using these routes that HIV first reached the cities. It was at first a disease of roadside and riverside brothels. Men were travelling in unprecedented numbers and single women were selling their bodies. From the cities it quickly spread to the Caribbean and North America. In America, the newly liberated gay movement provided an ideal amplifier for the virus. With a typically male affection for casual sex uninhibited by women, gay men in the United States had begun to invent a lifestyle unprecedented in its promiscuity. Some claimed hundreds or even thousands of sexual partners in their lives. Having rid themselves of prejudice about their sexual orientation, they were not about to heed warnings of disease. Chancroid, gonorrhoea, cytomegalovirus, herpes, chlamydia and other sexually transmitted diseases began to rise rapidly: by 12 per cent a year among American gay men in the late 1970s. One gay pop singer who had had 3,000 sexual partners admitted that he had also contracted hepatitis A and B, herpes, warts, Giardia, syphilis, gonorrhoea, chlamydia, cytomegalovirus and Epstein-Barr virus, not to mention various undiagnosed infections. AIDS merely joined the queue.

As the epidemic continued, AIDS changed little. Aside from the shared needles of heroin addicts and the shared blood products of haemophiliacs, it did not invent new means of spreading and it penetrated traditional, rural, monogamous societies very little. Only in parts of Central Africa torn apart by war did the disease become common outside big cities. In this there was an important lesson for the future. In retrospect, if you had been asked to predict how a new disease would strike the modern world, you would have to conclude that it would be sexual. In the twentieth century we made it harder for diseases to spread by insect, by water and (perhaps) by sneezing and direct contact. But we made it easier for them to spread by sex. We have, you might almost say, been lucky that only one lethal virus has appeared to exploit this opportunity.

Chapter 4
The Haemorrhagic Fevers

AIDS raised the prospect that the threat from infectious disease might come not from the reappearance of old diseases, but from the sudden emergence of new ones, or at least unrecognized ones. Hence the excitement over Lassa fever, Ebola virus and Hanta virus – an excitement which suddenly exploded after the AIDS epidemic, although each had first appeared long before AIDS. These three groups of viruses between them fuelled much of the alarmism of the 'diseases are coming' publishing boom of the mid-1990s. They are in essence very similar.

Each of these haemorrhagic fevers was as lethal as bubonic plague, at least at first. One Ebola outbreak killed more than 90 per cent of those infected. They all kill in much the same way: by causing the leakage of blood or fluid from the damaged blood vessels. Each spreads by aerosols (infected droplets from the lungs) or by direct contact with the infected blood and fluids of the victim. And each had gone unrecognized until the advent of modern microbiological techniques, when the viruses could at last be isolated.

Hanta virus and Lassa fever, like the Bolivian (Machupo) and Argentine (Junin) haemorrhagic fevers, are diseases of rodents, especially mice and voles. They are caught directly from the excreta of these animals by people living in rural areas and then spread person to person. Terrifying as they are, they have never managed to turn into major epidemics. Lassa fever causes frequent but limited outbreaks in West Africa, Machupo burned fiercely through the Bolivian town of San Joaquin in 1962, a Hanta virus killed 121 American soldiers in the Korean War and another caused a rapid epidemic that struck eighty people in the western United States in 1993.

It is unknown what would happen if an epidemic of one of these diseases occurred in a large city (although in 1989 a Lassa fever victim did spend some weeks seeking diagnosis and treatment in Chicago hospitals without infecting anybody before he died), but the chances of any of them developing the infectivity of flu are remote. First, they incapacitate their victims quickly, which is a big mistake for diseases that wish to be spread. Only if you can be sure that mosquitoes (in the case of malaria) or sewage pipes (in the case of cholera) will carry you away does it pay to lay your victims low. All aerosol-transmitted diseases have an interest in keeping their victims active – as colds do. Second, the haemorrhagic fevers kill too quickly. This facilitates the doctors' task of tracking down the victim's contacts. Asymptomatic carriers are an essential element of many diseases – Typhoid Mary being a good example. Mary Mallon was a New York cook who did not wash her hands and infected seven families in 1906 with the typhoid of which she was an asymptomatic carrier.

Ebola virus deserves special consideration. Together with Marburg virus, which killed some monkey handlers and their contacts in Germany in 1967, it comes from a family called the filoviruses. There have been almost annual outbreaks, the latest being those in Kikwit, Zaire (1995) and Gabon (1994–6). More than 200 people died in the Kikwit outbreak, which started with a forest charcoal worker. But antibodies in the blood of pygmies shows that the disease has probably been endemic in Central Africa for a long time. The animal reservoir remains unknown for certain, but all indications point at the bats. When artificially infected with the virus, all animals and plants so far tried either die or kill the virus – except bats. Bats infected with Ebola remain healthy but reproduce the virus in large quantities. Moreover, the only locations where known index cases probably caught the virus (on two occasions in both cases) were bat-infested: the Kitum cave on Mount Elgon and the Nzara cotton factory in Sudan.

Quite how the virus spreads from bats to human beings is uncertain, but in several cases it has come via monkeys or apes. Ebola is as lethal to other primates as it is to people, but it is from infected and dying primates that people have usually caught the disease. Perhaps the primates catch the disease from fruit licked by fruit bats during the previous night. In the latest outbreak, in Gabon in 1994, the epidemic began with a man who hunted and ate a chimpanzee.

So why, after centuries of slow-burn in the rainforest, did Ebola suddenly mount eight brief epidemics in twenty years? Is it, as some have suggested, a sort of ecological revenge by the wounded ecosystem of a ravished planet, a punishment for our transgression upon nature? No. The answer is simple, disturbing and deeply ironic. The cause of Ebola virus's new ability to break out is modern medicine. What happened in Yambuku is typical. A man walked into a mission hospital complaining of fever. The sisters gave him an injection of quinine. He was one of hundreds of patients injected that day. In a part of Zaire with no access to medical care at all, the mission hospital was overwhelmed with requests which the sisters were loath to refuse. But they had few hypodermic needles, and time was short so the needles were sterilized only once a day. In the queue behind the man, there was perhaps a pregnant woman who had come for a regular jab with B vitamins. The same needle was used for both. Three-quarters of those who caught the Ebola virus caught it from the nuns' needles: 92 per cent of those who caught it this way died.

In Sudan, it was a similar hospital that amplified the disease, and again in Kikwit more recently. In Marburg and Reston it was the trade in monkeys for medical research that brought the virus to the West. Modern medicine, not ecological disturbance, gave us Ebola epidemics. With this lesson learnt, the future of Ebola virus is clear. It will be like the Mount Elgon cases: single victims will walk into hospitals to die in agony, but, treated with care and caution, they will infect nobody else. A global pandemic of Ebola virus is highly unlikely.

Chapter 5
Plagues of the Future

So, if not Ebola, where is the next plague to come from? A coherent guess must identify a type of pathogen, an animal species from which it would jump, a method of transmission, and a new human habit that makes it possible for the epidemic to gain an unprecedented foothold in our species. There can be no doubt that we are a tempting target. Six billion individuals, many of them constantly jetting backwards and forwards between continents, constitute a single herd of vast proportions. The rewards for a germ that colonized us would be immense. It would quickly become one of the most successful microbes in history.

First, the type of pathogen. By and large, we have found large parasites easier to deal with than small ones (and, to extend the point, we have also found predators easier to deal with than parasites). This is perhaps because of their complex life cycles. Tape worms, round worms and hook worms – the really big parasites – have been fairly easily defeated in most countries. Smaller invertebrate parasites, like the flukes that cause schistosomiasis and the worms that cause river blindness (onchocerciasis), are more problematic, but are generally retreating in more areas than they are advancing. They have rarely caused epidemic plagues. Fungi and yeasts, too, are not much of a threat and never really have been. Protozoa are more intractable enemies: malaria, sleeping sickness, Chagas' disease, Leishmaniasis and amoebic dysentery in particular. They are not usually difficult to treat, but they are hard to prevent. Until very recently they evaded all attempts to vaccinate. A malaria vaccine may at last have been minted. Called the 'Columbian' vaccine it has shown promise in field trials in Tanzania.

Serious as they are, most protozoan diseases are not new. With the exception of Leishmaniasis, which first appeared in India in 1824, they are 'heirlooms' that have been with us for aeons. Much the same can be said of bacterial diseases, on the next step down in size (most bacteria are about one-tenth the length of most protozoa). Although bacteria have mounted some remarkable insect-borne and aerosol-spread epidemics – bubonic plague and tuberculosis, for example – their speciality is the water-borne disease: cholera, typhoid and shigella dysentery. We have on the whole found ways to close that niche. Emerging bacterial diseases tend to be newly virulent forms of old diseases (such as E[scherichia] coli 0157:H7, which first kidnapped virulent genes from shigella dysentery in about 1982) or bacteria exploiting highly specialized new niches such as Legionella. Moreover, antibiotics have given us a formidable armoury against bacteria. Some are hard to treat, others quickly devise resistance to many or all antibiotics, but it would be very surprising if a brand-new human bacterial epidemic appeared and was as incurable as AIDS, for instance.

By far the greatest new source of threat to our species comes from the smallest of all our enemies, the viruses (a virus is one-hundredth the length of a typical bacterium).

Not only do viruses specialize in causing the rapid epidemics of aerosol crowd disease that we are ideally suited to entertaining (things like measles, influenza, colds), but viruses are also peculiarly intractable. They do not have a biochemistry set of their own which we can attack: they use ours instead. To attack their metabolism is therefore to attack our own. This is why antivirals have never rivalled antibiotics in their efficiency, and medicine has truly cured very few viral diseases. The list of antiviral chemicals is short – interferon, gangcyclovir, ribavirin, acyclovir, AZT, DDI and protease inhibitors – and most are only partly effective. Viruses also seem to have less trouble jumping species than larger parasites do. A catalogue of the emerging diseases that keep epidemiologists awake at night is dominated by viruses: AIDS, influenza, Ebola, Lassa, Hanta, monkeypox, rabies, dengue, Rift Valley and so on.

So it will be a virus. Which animal species will be the reservoir? Virtually all new diseases begin as zoonoses: infections caught directly from other animals. We may have already acquired diseases from or exchanged diseases with dogs (measles), cows (smallpox, tuberculosis), pigs (which refracted duck influenza), ducks (influenza), rats (plague, typhus), horses (some colds, equine encephalitis), mice (Lassa fever, Hanta viruses), monkeys (yellow fever, monkeypox) and bats (rabies, Ebola). There is an obvious bias in this list towards domesticated creatures, and one estimate places the total number of diseases we have acquired from our domesticated animals at 300, with another 100 caught from wild species. Because of the biochemical similarities, closely related species are a greater risk than distant relatives, which is why so few poultry diseases spread to human beings and why mammals are the most frequent source. Gregarious species such as bats and cattle are also more apt to supply us with germs suited to exploiting our crowded cities. Solitary habits, like those of cats, militate against contagious epidemics. And, finally, tropical species are more dangerous reservoirs than cold-climate or (especially) mountain species such as sheep.

I see little risk from domesticated animals; our contact with them was far more intimate and frequent in classical and medieval times. We have harvested what we can from cattle and pigs in the way of pathogens and parasites (though food-poisoning from industrial abattoirs is a special case). Our contact with wild animals also was more intimate in the Stone Age, when hunting was a staple means of earning a living. But in those days we lived in scattered rural communities. Perhaps today a disease that could not sustain an epidemic in a village will reach a city instead.

So we can narrow the search for a source of new disease to the following description: it will be a mammal, living in the tropics, that gathers in large flocks and has until now had little contact with our species. My money is on bats. Nearly one in every four mammal species is a bat, so probably one-quarter of all mammal diseases are in bats. Rabies and Ebola are not the only diseases to have jumped from bats to humans. Australia has encountered two brand-new bat viruses in two years, both of which origi-nated with flying foxes (fruit bats) in sub-tropical Queens-land. One was equine morbilivirus, which killed fourteen horses and one human being in 1994. Two years later, a woman who cared for sick bats at an animal sanctuary died from a virus of the same family as rabies: a lyssavirus. If I were writing a screenplay for a scary new film about a disease, I would set the opening scene in an animal sanctuary. Such places did not exist a generation ago. They are ideal marketplaces for wild animals to give their diseases to human beings.

Chapter 6
Contagion in the Third Millennium

This new disease would be a virus whose mode of transmission would have to be precisely right to work in the modern world. Insect vectors are one possibility. In the 1960s and 1970s, new 'arboviruses' – arthropod-borne viruses – were appearing (or at least being identified) at an astonishing rate: over 500 have now been recognized, of which 120 can cause human disease. For instance, mosquitoes transmit various forms of potentially lethal viral encephalitis from mammals to people. There have been recent outbreaks of such encephalitis in every continent except Antarctica.

Some of these encephalitis viruses are highly virulent. Rift Valley fever is spread by *Aedes* mosquitoes from new lakes created by dams. The Aswan dam in Egypt and the Diama dam in Mauretania each caused epidemics of Rift Valley fever when they were completed – though the epidemics quickly declined as fish populations expanded and reduced the numbers of mosquitoes in the lakes. Eastern Equine encephalitis, caught from horses in America, kills up to 80 per cent of its human victims. Borna disease virus, also caught from horses (though not necessarily via mosquitoes) in Germany and Japan has been associated with severe depression and mental illness (see p. 43). It homes in on the limbic system of the brain, where mood is determined. Viruses love infecting the nervous system, because nerves form such easy paths along which to spread, bypassing the blood with its patrolling immune cells.

But other arboviruses have developed a special ability to attack the blood, causing haemorrhagic fever. Oropouche virus, which has afflicted 200,000 people in Amazonia, is spread by midges that breed in the tiny puddles inside cacao bean husks. Heaps of these husks outside villages caused a population explosion of the biting midges near human habitation. They brought the virus from the blood of sloths, their more usual source of meals. In Australia there are other mosquito-borne diseases, transmitted from kangaroos: Ross River and Barmah forest viruses in particular. They cause a form of virulent arthritis, which has turned epidemic in parts of the Pacific to which its vector has been introduced.

Mosquitoes and midges are not the only arthropods to carry viral fevers. Crimean-Congo haemorrhagic fever, which is caught from infected ticks mostly in desert parts of Western Asia, has a habit of infecting surgeons who operate on patients thinking their haemorrhages can be repaired. Lyme disease, a rickettsia (small bacterium) that causes fever and arthritis which can be fatal, also spreads by means of ticks from deer in Europe and Asia. Its sudden resurgence in recent years has been caused by the recovery of deer numbers. It is now the commonest arthropod-borne disease in America.

Yet, because so few people now harbour, let alone share, fleas and lice and because ticks and mosquitoes are mostly a rural or seasonal problem, this long list of horrible afflictions probably contains none that can sustain a major human plague. It is doubtful if any of them are even new, though some, such as Lyme and Ross River, have certainly become commoner.

It is true that malaria thrives in the tropics and once thrived in temperate countries. Indeed, certain kinds of malaria are equipped with a feature specially designed to enable them to survive during northern winters when no mosquitoes are about – a long dormant period in the liver of their host. But malaria died out in the temperate world long before effective drugs were used against it. The reason is that people gradually improved their defences against mosquito invasion. First, they drained the marshes where the mosquitoes bred. To this day in tropical countries there is a clear correlation between population density and malaria: the denser human populations become, the fewer malaria cases there are, because the mosquitoes' breeding sites are built on, cultivated or drained. Population growth is the enemy of malaria. Moreover, malaria died out in Northern Europe because the *Anopheles* mosquitoes found cattle in barns a more easy source of blood than people, and switched their habits. This was a disaster for the malaria plasmodium, because it cannot survive in cattle, and the mosquitoes, replete with cow blood, stopped biting people.

This illustrates the real problem for diseases with using mosquitoes to ferry you about. You have to infect the animal that the mosquito bites most. If you do not, then you will eventually lose out in competition to another strain of pathogen that does infect that species. There is room in each genus of mosquito for only one kind of malaria. This is why the bite of by far the commonest kind of mosquito, *Culex*, is mostly harmless. *Culex* mosquitoes carry avian malaria, which they transmit to birds. *Anopheles*, which at some point in the past must have found itself biting monkeys and apes more often than birds, carries primate malaria. *Aedes*, another genus, is almost a domesticated mosquito, which prefers to breed in man-made receptacles like water butts, old tyres and tanks. This made it almost inevitable that it would carry human diseases and sure enough different *Aedes* species carry yellow fever and dengue fever. They crossed the Atlantic with their insect vector in the slave trade and became the curse of the Caribbean and Central America. In the nineteenth century, thousands died in epidemics that afflicted cities as far north as Memphis and Philadelphia. Yellow fever defeated the first attempts at building the Panama canal, where it was eventually quelled by rigorous control of man-made mosquito breeding sites. But yellow fever has resisted efforts to eradicate it in the New World by taking refuge in wild monkeys, from where mosquito-bitten rainforest loggers still bring it back to cities. Epidemics continue in the Old World, as well: 30,000 died in Ethiopia in the 1960s.

Dengue fever uses the same *Aedes* mosquitoes, a new and aggressive species of which, called the Asian tiger, has been spreading in North America. This has led some to prognosticate a new epidemic, and a far more dangerous form of dengue has appeared and spread from the Philippines. In 1981, this form of dengue infected nearly 400,000 people in Cuba; in 1995, it infected 30,000 in Venezuela. This disease is actually an immune overreaction to infection with two successive strains of dengue.

Despite these problems, I still say there is little prospect of a new mosquito-borne disease spilling out of the developing world and into the West. The scarcity of mosquitoes in densely populated, urban centres, the ease with which new insecticides could be deployed in an emergency (notwithstanding the problems of mosquito resistance to some older insecticides) and the general precautions that most town people now take against being frequently bitten, make it unlikely that such a new virus could take off in American or European towns in the way that yellow fever did in the past. And it is a prerequisite of an emerging plague that it must be a crowd disease capable of spreading in urban areas.

Insect-borne diseases are often highly virulent. They do not get 'tamer' as the years go by. Malaria, yellow fever, bubonic plague and typhus are among the most lethal of all infections and have shown no signs of declining virulence over the centuries. There is a good reason for this: laying low the victim, sending him to a flea-ridden bed or into a mosquito-indifferent delirium, is actually to the pathogen's advantage. It increases the chance he will be bitten again. The victim's death in the process has no consequence for the germ. It does not need him to be healthy in order to spread the infection – though it does need the insect to be healthy, which is why malaria kills or incapacitates people, but does not hurt mosquitoes.

For much the same reasons, water-borne diseases are also virulent. They spread not in the bodies of their victims, but in their sewage. An immobilized and dying victim is no drawback. But water-borne plagues are now equally unlikely and for similar reasons. On the whole sanitation is improving, even in the poorest parts of the world, and those diseases that could go pandemic like cholera, typhoid and dysentery have long since sung their best arias. Isolated bursts of cholera are still possible and new crises caused by creatures that specialize in public water systems, such as cryptosporidium, are even likely. But we must look elsewhere for the true danger.

Aerosol diseases are enjoying the modern world immensely. Frequent, rapid travel has vastly multiplied the number of strangers we each meet in our daily lives. Cities are constantly exchanging bodies with other cities all across the world. By the year 2000, there will be 600 million person-trips on international flights every year. It is, in theory, a paradise for air-transmitted infections. Colds, in particular, can cross oceans and continents in a matter of hours, infecting the whole globe in weeks. Flu strains can do the same. On one flight, grounded in Alaska for three hours while repairs were carried out, nearly three-quarters of the passengers caught influenza from one person. The possibility therefore remains that a new disease, with the characteristic contagion of a cold or a flu, could sweep the planet in a month. If it were lethal, the death toll can be imagined.

That is roughly what happened in 1918. A new strain of an old disease, influenza, arose in Chinese pigs who had caught it from ducks. Called H1N1, it had mutated its surface protein genes in such a way as to escape existing immune defence and simultaneously attack in a much more virulent way than normal. For the first time influenza could kill not just the old, the very young and the weak but healthy adults as well. It ravaged the troops in the trenches, spread to cities all around the world and killed more people in six months than the worst war the world had ever known had claimed in four years. As it spread, so did herd immunity, with the result that it became harder and harder for viruses to find new susceptible hosts. The epidemic died gradually away.

Two new varieties of flu have since come out of China: H2N2 in 1957 and H3N2 in 1968. In 1977 H1N1 reappeared, presaging, or so it seemed, another virulent pandemic. But nothing happened. America's health establishment cried Wolf! and lost face. The harmlessness of the new 'swine fever' flu epidemic of 1977 remains as great a puzzle as the virulence of it in 1918. To this day many health professionals are extremely nervous of new strains of flu. There is nothing to stop another virulent one sweeping the world even more rapidly than it did in 1918. In wild waterfowl that migrate north through China, there are scores of strains. The marshy areas where they rest on their long flights are epicentres of such unnumbered H and N types. These areas are fairly far from human habitation, almost by definition. But it would take little for domestic ducks to pick up a new strain, mix and reassort it with domestic pigs and pass on to human beings a more than usually virulent strain.

Is it just luck that none of the emerging diseases to threaten us in recent years have been as casually contagious as influenza? I suspect not. Highly contagious epidemics with high mortality are rare. Only smallpox, measles and flu meet the criteria. Two of those showed rapid evolution to lower virulence and the third, smallpox, also decreased in virulence, though less rapidly. There is a tendency for highly contagious diseases to be tame, for the same reasons that insect-borne diseases refuse to be tamed: the more they keep their victims healthy, the better they spread. Our species is now so full of mild, contagious infections, which we call colds, bugs, flus and 'dreaded lurgis', that there may be relatively little room for other, more vicious ones to catch on. Diseases, after all, are in competition with each other for the scarce resource of our bodies' fluids.

Chapter 7
The Virulence Enigma

It is worth looking at disease from the germ's point of view. Living inside the human body is a hard enough challenge. The body has formidable weapons at its disposal. It can raise its own temperature to a level at which the germ's own fragile proteins start to fall apart. This, we now know, is the point of fever: it is a defence, rather than just a symptom. Studies show that trying to lower people's temperatures during infections merely prolongs and may even worsen the infection. The body can also sequester the blood's free iron into a form that the germ cannot get at. Infectious bacteria are dependent on finding iron. Thus the fact that the dissolved-iron content of blood falls during an infection is again a defence, not an effect of the disease. Studies show that giving patients iron supplements is counterproductive.

These are just the first line of defence. Then the germ must dodge the immune system, which has three strong lines of fortification. Its first is the mucosal immune cells: patrolling squads of cells in the mucus of throat, gut and other surfaces, intent on keeping these vulnerable areas sterile. Then comes the antibody system: a whole chemical assembly line producing whatever highly specific protein designs best smother the proteins on the surfaces of bacteria and viruses. Finally, if the germ beats that, there is the cellular immune system, a poorly understood array of bug-eating white blood cells, carefully distinguishing self from non-self.

This is all very ingenious – and it begins to become clear why new diseases do not appear every week – but having gained entry, survived the fever, found a secure refuge and avoided alerting an immune response, the germ still has its hardest task to do. Its whole future, and that of its offspring, depends on being able to come out of hiding at just the right time and in just the right place to jump into a new individual. Thus certain kinds of malaria take care to emerge from their refuge in the liver after a year's wait, the better to be around when the summer and mosquitoes are back. Typhoid in the temperate regions has invented the ability to lurk, symptomless, in the gall bladder, so as to re-emerge later when the chance of infecting another host might be greater. Herpes takes care to migrate to the surface along nerves that serve the mouth and the genitals – places where contact with other people is likely. In every case, the germ's most important adaptation is that which enables it to cross the inhospitable space between the bodies of its victims.

The answer would seem to be easy: the germ should evolve the ability to survive in the air or on the ground at all temperatures and in all conditions of humidity and despite the best efforts of chemical companies to disinfect it. Yet this does not happen. Germs are amazingly fastidious. Some can survive only in genital mucus yet cannot even live on a toilet seat for a few moments. Some require a mosquito of exactly the right genus. Some spread by droplets sneezed from the nose and mouth yet last no more than a few minutes in the open before dying. Why is this? Why do colds not have the durability of anthrax, or malaria the ability to be sneezed? The answer is wonderfully elegant when it dawns on you. For most pathogens the closest thing they have to an enemy is other pathogens of the same species. Just like rabbits or mosquitoes they compete with each other to become ancestors. Those that are best at it eventually crowd out those that are less effective. Suppose two tuberculosis bacteria have equal ability to spread in sneezes, but one of them also has the ability to survive for several years if it falls on barren ground. This ability comes at a price: it requires some extra machinery which takes a little time and energy to make. So it will actually spread more slowly than its more vulnerable cousin, because the short-lived bacterium can reproduce faster. Nature is a ruthless economist, stripping away all unnecessary features to make its products compete. Parasites become beautifully adapted to one method of transmission that works at the expense of the ability to use other methods. Sexually transmitted diseases gradually lose the ability to spread by aerosol and vice versa.

So the anxiety that AIDS would suddenly become a disease that could be carried by mosquitoes, or could be spread by aerosol, is largely misplaced. Diseases only very rarely change their modes of transmission. If an aerosol disease is to cause a plague it will not be AIDS, typhus or yellow fever; it will be one that is already spread by aerosol: influenza, for example.

Moreover, there is good reason to believe that aerosol and direct-contact diseases are getting milder in virulence, not stronger.

In large, crowded medieval cities with many people

rubbing shoulders day and night, sharing beds or living five to a room, germs could afford to be as vicious as smallpox: ill people still touched lots of others. But in the modern suburb, where the average person has direct physical contact with almost nobody except his immediate family, a germ cannot afford to incapacitate its victims at all, because otherwise it will never get to spread by skin-to-skin contact. That is why cold viruses now thrive, using only the occasional contact between active people in playground or workplace to spread.

It is therefore no accident that many diseases did not just become rarer in the West during the nineteenth and early twentieth centuries as living standards rose, hygiene improved and crowding declined – they also became milder. The virulence of diphtheria, typhoid, tuberculosis, scarlet fever, whooping cough and many other diseases declined steadily after the middle of the nineteenth century. In these diseases more than three-quarters of the decline in deaths occurred before the appearance of drugs in the 1930s. About the only exception was polio, which for unknown reasons is more virulent in adults than children, leaving the gut and attacking the nervous system, so improved hygiene led to people catching it later in life and therefore more severely. By the early 1950s, 60,000 Americans caught polio each year and it was the most feared of all diseases.

It is also no accident that the sudden appearance of a highly virulent strain of flu coincided with a return to conditions of squalor, crowding and poor hygiene: the trenches, troopships and camps of the First World War. It is, I submit, no surprise that H1N1 flu was milder when it returned in 1977 and that no other really virulent flu strain has come out of China since 1918.

For this reason – that casual-contact diseases are mild and getting milder – I rule out the plague of the third millennium being such a germ, and I even rashly assert that a return of virulent influenza is unlikely. Casual-contact diseases will continue to afflict us; indeed, they will thrive as never before in airliners, offices and above all schools. We place our children together in herds called nurseries, with much traffic between them, at the age at which they are unusually free with their saliva and unusually keen on body contact. But the bugs that enjoy these opportunities will not often kill us. We are more use to them soldiering on despite a 'nasty cold'.

So, if insect-borne germs are going to be virulent but local, water-borne diseases rare and casual-contact diseases mild but common, that leaves one method of transmission: sex. We need no reminder that we live in an age of sexually transmitted infection. AIDS is not alone. Scores of nasty infections have been on the increase because of our changing sexual habits: chlamydia, herpes, genital warts, yeast infections, hepatitis B, chancroid and others. Only gonorrhoea and syphilis have continued to decline. Never before, in the history of the world – not even in the heyday of syphilis – has sex been so risky. The reason for this is partly the greater promiscuity of the modern age: promiscuous heterosexual sex unleashed by the contraceptive pill in the 1960s and promiscuous gay sex unleashed by gay rights campaigns in the 1970s multiplied manyfold the opportunities for pathogens in the West. But there is another, larger reason. When a woman has sex with a man in the modern urban West, each of them could have just been travelling in a distant continent. As far as sexually transmitted pathogens are concerned, the world has become a village. The 'herd' available to an organism has become so much greater that diseases which do not even have means of persisting silently can now sustain epidemics. The vast ingenuity of syphilis, in concealing itself for years inside the body, is no longer a prerequisite of a sexually transmitted disease. Something as unsubtle as yeast can do as well. Nonetheless, for a virulent plague, the ability to make asymptomatic individuals infectious is very valuable. The remarkable thing about AIDS, which made it so resistant to preventive measures, was how little effect it had on its victims for the first few months and even years. This latent time, during which it survived inside T cells, was a form of weakness: the virus could not overcome the antibodies of the host. But, for a sexually transmitted disease, it was also an advantage. It enabled the virus to overcome the problem of spreading to entirely new sexual partners of the victim. By the time symptoms appeared, even quite monogamous individuals had often infected several people.

The one thing that sexually transmitted diseases find very hard to do is jump between species, for obvious reasons. It is possible that AIDS came into the human species by sex, but more likely that there was some kind of blood mixing in the first cases. For this reason, although new sexually transmitted plagues would make short work of such a tempting target as the modern human race, there is not a ready supply of them. Bats, for example, may be equipped with a variety of virulent sexually transmitted diseases, but we would be unlikely to acquire them that way. It is by this thread that our future hangs. We must hope that new sexually transmitted viruses never find the opportunity to pass from other mammals to us.

But mention of blood mixing brings me to needles. We have invented all sorts of entirely new ways of spreading disease: modes of transmission that were not available to diseases in the past. Open surgery, injections and air-conditioning systems are three obvious avenues for bugs worth their salt. We provide ourselves with services – water, air, food – from systems of great complexity in which a single location may serve a whole herd and in which much emphasis is placed on sterility. Sterility to bugs is another word for invitation. It means vacant niche. And when members of our species get sick or weak we pack them off to buildings full of other sick or weak people, called hospitals, all the better to share any germs among the most vulnerable.

Various germs have tried to exploit each of these vulner-abilities. Compulsory mass education has undoubtedly been of enormous benefit to rhinoviruses, which cause most colds, not to mention all sorts of other germs. An average schoolchild catches maybe eight such viruses each year, a number that would undoubtedly seem astonishing even to our great-grandparents, let alone to our Stone Age ancestors.

As for our mass-distribution systems, Legionella has gone for air conditioners, cryptosporidium for clean-water sys-tems and E. coli 157 for huge modern abattoirs where it can jump in a flash from faeces to meat intended for a score of cities. Each of these deserves credit for ingenuity and skill, but none has yet managed to cause more than a local nuisance to the human race. Legionella killed thirty-four in its first recognized outbreak in Philadelphia in 1976 and continues to plague air-conditioning systems to this day; cryptosporidium laid 400,000 low in Milwaukee in 1993, and has shown a remarkable ability to invent chlorine-resistant strains. E. coli 157 killed nineteen people in Scotland in 1996–7 and seems to find abattoirs, however clean, the perfect environment to pass from faeces to meat.

We should not neglect the gallant effort of BSE, the most bizarre disease of all because it seems not to possess any genetic material, just a rogue form of protein that catalyses its own creation. BSE took splendid advantage of a closed cycle created when cattle offal was fed to cattle without being heated sufficiently to kill the protein. An epidemic resulted in cattle, but failed to spread to human beings in any numbers. By mid-1997 there had been fewer than twenty cases of 'new variant' Creutzfeldt-Jakob disease, the kind apparently caused by eating infected beef.

As for hospitals, the opportunities for ambitious pathogens are immense. True, since doctors were bludgeoned into hygiene during the nineteenth century, the days when scarlet fever and childbed fever could move from one patient to another on the apron of a doctor who had just done an autopsy are long gone. The danger of shared needles has been recognized, too, even in remote mission hospitals. But, even so, hospitals are the perfect environment for many strains of disease to turn virulent. There is a steady supply of new, vulnerable hosts and all sorts of mechanisms for germs to spread from one person to another. Immunosuppressive drugs used during transplants make weak people still more vulnerable to infection, and open surgery makes it far easier for a bacterium to gain access to body cavities, bypassing the defences in the body's skin and mucus. The frequent prophylactic use of antibiotics selects for strains of germ that cannot be easily killed. Nearly one in twenty Americans who goes into hospital catches an infectious disease while there. In other parts of the world, the proportion is probably greater. These so-called 'nosocomial' infections include staphylococcus, streptococcus, hepatitis B, pseudomonas, clostridium and E. coli 157. However sterile we make our hospitals, however rigorous we make our procedures and however well we educate each other about dangers, hospitals represent, for virus diseases, an enormous opportunity – and evolution is adept at exploiting opportunities.

Chapter 8
The Task of Sisyphus

Not all emerging diseases cause new symptoms. In recent years there has been a growing recognition that all sorts of diseases that were once thought to be nothing to do with infection may actually be caused by viruses or bacteria. The comfortable distinction between infectious disease, which people used to die of, and non-infectious disease, which people now die of, is breaking down.

The most dramatic case of this is ulcers. Pharmaceutical companies grew rich on ulcer drugs designed to fight the acid that supposedly caused them. It now turns out that this was treating the symptoms, not the cause, and that by far the most important cause of duodenal and to a lesser extent gastric ulcers is a simple bacterium called Helico-bacter, easily killed by certain antibiotics.

Browse through the medical literature and you will find frequent hints that other diseases are about to be subject to the same revision. An obscure virus infecting nerve and brain cells called Borna disease has been killing horses and occasionally cats in the former East Germany. Now two studies have discovered that people subject to psychiatric illness may be infected with Borna virus. In the first study, in Germany, neuropsychiatric patients proved six times as likely as people at large to be carrying antibodies to the virus, and fully 30 per cent of those suffering acute depression had been infected with the virus. More convincing still, in people whose depression comes and goes the virus was active during their depressed phases and inactive during their normal phases. The same news comes from Japan, where schizophrenics as well as depressives are far more likely to have the Borna virus than the public at large. The Japanese scientists thought it might be something to do with eating horseflesh raw, but they found that virtually everybody in their sample regularly ate raw horse so they cannot tell if that is what makes them depressed.

The Borna virus is not going to be the whole answer and the suggestion that people might catch it from horses rather than from each other is premature. But for those who are struck, like a bolt from the blue, with a sudden and inexplicable burst of severe depression, the explanation that it was a germ they caught, rather than something they ate, remembered from their childhood or brought upon themselves by worrying too much, will perhaps be a crumb of comfort.

Other diseases that might prove to be caused largely by germs include rheumatoid arthritis, Crohn's disease, diabetes mellitus and several cancers including lymphoma, leukaemia and cervical cancer. Suspicion is growing that many cases of kidney failure, stroke and hypertension are actually caused by Hanta viruses and their relatives. We have only just begun to realize how important infectious proteins (prions) may be in causing neurological disease – not just Creutzfeldt-Jakob disease, but perhaps Parkinson's and Alzheimer's diseases as well. Even heart disease, that most occupational of hazards, may have a strong infectious component. Chlamydia, cytomegalovirus and herpes have been implicated in causing or worsening the atherosclerosis that leads to heart attacks. A study published in 1997 showed that antibiotics that kill chlamydia can reduce the risk of heart attacks by 30 per cent.

For all the emergence of new diseases, some are also disappearing. Like any other species, they are vulnerable to extinction. Smallpox is already extinct in the wild and polio will soon follow it, both driven there by vaccination. But the extinction of a disease merely opens an opportunity for another disease. The disappearance of smallpox means that more and more children are now growing up unvaccinated. Monkeypox, a closely related disease of monkeys, is therefore presented with a tempting target. Sure enough, in 1997, the first widespread epidemic of monkeypox was reported from Zaire: at least 160 people were infected.

Medicine has underestimated not only the prevalence of infectious disease but the resourcefulness of it as well. The enemy is not a static, fixed, finite force, but an infinitely inventive complex of genetic combinations engaged in a massive campaign of trial and error. That is what natural selection is. The whole point of being a parasite is to make a living inside a host. The stakes may seem high to us, the hosts, as we face the AIDS epidemic or remember the Black Death, but they are much higher for the two germs in question. Breeding within our bodies, passing through more generations in one epidemic than we have passed through since the beginning of recorded history, they evolve at a far more rapid rate. They need to, because the parasitic lifestyle is an immensely difficult one to achieve. Not only must the organism evade or overcome the host's defences, it must then change tactics altogether and find a way to move to a new host, and not just any new host but one that has not already acquired immunity.

Effective antibiotics merely put bacteria under evolutionary pressure to invent a way round them. The more widely the drug is used, the more likely it is that it will stop working well. This is a concept people have had great trouble understanding. It is an arms race. The enemy changes. Or, as the Red Queen put it in *Through the Looking Glass*, 'Here, you see, it takes all the running you can do, to keep in the same place.' Doctors have tended to act like engineers and treat germs as static enemies. Imagine if every time you invented a new way of pumping water, the water found a new way of not being pumped. That is the reality of medical treatment. Indeed, the analogy is surprisingly apt. Some of the drug-resistance strains of bacteria are equipped with special molecular pumps, which expel the drug from the bacterial cell as fast as it comes in. Others are more precise, disabling the drug by digesting it with special enzymes. Like the legendary Sisyphus in Hades, medicine is condemned to keep rolling a stone up to the top of a hill only to see it roll back down again.

Moreover, bacteria seem to engage in a sort of genetic free trade, whereby they ingest genes from each other, particularly in the form of 'plasmids' – closed loops of DNA. Many resistance genes are on such plasmids. Good plasmids, like good technological products in world trade, spread rapidly. Bacteria do not need to rely on their own inventiveness; they can copy it from others. Nor should it be forgotten that antibiotics are natural substances. Most are found in soil fungi, which use them to fight chemical warfare against bacteria in the soil. Resistance is therefore an ancient characteristic that many bacteria have possessed for along time. Parasitic bacteria, not encountering fungi in our bodies, dropped their resistance to save energy for other things. This often meant just switching off the genes concerned. Switching them back on again was a simple evolutionary step once they were being put to the sword by drugs.

Strains of bacteria resistant to antibiotics are encouraged by the misuse of the drugs. Every time you take antibiotics for a cold, which is a virus and therefore unaffected, you give the billions of bacteria in your body a quick training session in how to resist. You are making it that much harder to treat a future outbreak of bacterial disease in yourself. Every time you fail to complete a course of anti-tuberculosis treatment, you leave alive only the tuberculosis germs that have a slight ability to resist the drug. Every time a farmer doses his cattle with antibiotics merely to make them grow faster, he risks creating an untreatable strain of bacteria that could spread to human beings (although the evidence linking such growth promoters to antibiotic resistance does not so far exist).

Antibiotic resistance has emerged in most bacterial diseases, notably typhoid, gonorrhoea, pneumococcus pneumonia and tuberculosis. Staphylococcus has lost its susceptibility to penicillin almost everywhere. In 15 per cent of cases it is resistant to methicillin as well. Drug-resistant pneumococcus has been found in up to 50 per cent of samples in Spain, South Africa and Hungary. Streptococcus has achieved resistance to all but the newest antibiotics such as vancomycin. And vancomycin resistance has appeared in enterococcus bacteria already. It cannot be long before it spreads to even more dangerous pathogens. Tuberculosis is increasingly resistant in some patients to all drugs thrown at it. Rifampin, the last drug to resist resistance, has been around since the 1960s.

The problem is similar among protozoa, which have had little difficulty evolving resistance to most of the drugs we invent. Falciparum malaria, the most dangerous kind, may soon be resistant to all drugs except artemisinin and its relatives. The case is not helped by legal problems. The drug company Hoffman-La Roche is being sued over side-effects caused by mefloquine. If Roche loses and the drug is withdrawn, where will the next drug come from?

The eventual ineffectiveness of most or even all anti-microbials is certain. We are on a treadmill and we cannot stop it. If we are to keep infectious disease at bay we must invent new chemicals for ever. Unfortunately, that looks increasingly difficult. The rate of invention of new anti-biotics has slowed down measurably in recent years. There has been no new class of antibiotic since the carba-penemes, developed twenty years ago. The great age of antibiotics, during which 4,000 different chemicals were produced, ended in about 1975.

This is an alarming picture. Pessimists believe that we will look back with nostalgia to the age when antibiotics worked and that, as the next millennium unfolds, we will find ourselves back in a war of attrition with bacteria, afflicted for the first time in decades with dreadful prema-ture mortality. But this is a counsel of despair. It ignores the fact that changing lifestyles had already lifted the threat of bacterial disease substantially long before the invention of antibiotics. Tuberculosis was declining in Britain by 1920. Antibiotics did not even accelerate the decline. Even if they are incurable, bacterial diseases will be much scarcer and less virulent than they were in the days of slums, open sewers and flea bites. Besides, there has been a tendency to exaggerate the trend towards antibiotic resistance. It is not always an inexorable advance, but a sporadic and reversible process. Resistance appears in a hospital, gets worse for a while and then sometimes dies away, especially if the hospital ceases to use the drug in question. Resistance can be an expensive process to maintain, from the bacterial point of view; when it is no longer needed, the creatures tend to switch it off again.

Moreover, there is no reason on earth why we need to lose our ingenuity, just because our enemies have kept theirs. We should take a leaf out of their book, and analyse every trick they use to disable our poisons, the better to undo that trick. If, for instance, an antibiotic is resisted by an enzyme that takes it apart, then invent a new antibiotic that the enzyme cannot fit, or a chemical that attacks the enzyme. For example, amoxicillin is resisted by a bacterial enzyme called beta lactamase, which in turn is inhibited by a drug called clavumalate. Round three to us. If the drug is resisted by a pump that excludes the drug from the bacterial cell, then find a way to attack the pump. So clever are we getting at visualizing the true shapes of molecules that we no longer perfect chemicals by trial and error – as bacteria do – but by design. The age of unchallenged antibiotics may soon be over, but the age of other drugs is only just beginning. Monoclonal antibodies, haemopoietins and magainins (from toads) are antibacterial chemicals that we have barely begun to develop. As long as we recognize that we can never declare victory, and that each advance against disease will be followed by a later reverse, there is no reason why today's exploding biological research in the human world cannot stay one step ahead of the natural-selection research undertaken in the bacterial world.

There is a class of drugs on the horizon that shows special promise not only against bacteria, but against viruses as well: the DNA vaccines. DNA vaccines consist of small stretches of DNA code which carry the instructions for how to build particular proteins belonging to a parasite. Many viruses have proteins that do not work well as antigens – that is, they do not elicit an antibody response – perhaps because they lurk in crevices on the virus's coat where antibodies cannot get at them. Others – flu being a good example – have proteins that work well as antigens but they change so fast that immunity does not last; and they have other proteins, inside, that do not change so fast but are not accessible to the antibodies. So a scientist takes that protein, writes out the DNA recipe for making that protein, constructs the appropriate DNA message and fires it into a mouse on a particle of gold. What happens next is mysteriously fortunate. The DNA is absorbed by some of the mouse's cells and inside the cell it is treated like a normal gene: it is transcribed into RNA and translated into the protein again. That protein is somehow recognized as foreign and the immune system is alerted to kill the cell that has produced it. But it is a different part of the immune system that comes into play: the so-called MHC

Class I system. This generates an attack by whole white blood cells, not by antibodies. The reason for this is rather curious. During infancy, your body educates its immune system by teaching it which proteins are self and which are non-self. It does this by the simple, if ruthless, technique of destroying those T cells that recognize any home-made protein. This leaves only those T cells that recognize and attack non-self proteins. Make a human cell produce virus proteins and it is soon attacked by one of these T cells. Why this Class I attack works better than Class II attack from the antibodies remains enigmatic. But the important fact is that just such an experiment has rendered a mouse resistant to all strains of flu for at least a year.

It will be many more years of research before we are sure that DNA vaccines are safe and effective. Nonetheless, I am prepared to predict that DNA vaccines represent the future. For a start, DNA vaccines are cheaper, easier to prepare, less fragile, more easily stored and easier to transport than normal vaccines. They are more stable and long-lasting, which means they can be carried to remote, unrefrigerated clinics. A decade or two into the new millennium they will be standard treatment (or prevention) for viral diseases that are presently incurable and for bacterial diseases that have developed resistance to antibiotics. They are also showing promise already against an auto-immune disease that resembles multiple sclerosis in mice. But they are only the start. Reading the library of DNA that lies inside every organism is going to transform medicine and lead to cures, treatments and vaccines we cannot even imagine. Far from looking back at the late twentieth century as a golden age of medicine, we will look back in contempt at the primitive, ineffective and costly tools that were then available.

Ah, cost. The last and best argument of the pessimist. What use is a therapy for a viral disease if it costs six months' wages for the typical inhabitant of an African country? Extraordinary advances have now been made with AIDS treatment. Protease inhibitors can halt and perhaps even reverse the progress of the virus in a patient's body. AIDS will soon no longer be an incurable disease. But protease inhibitors are immensely expensive: a course of treatment costs many thousands of dollars. What use is that to a truck driver in Zaire, or a prostitutue in Bombay? Drugs such as these, even if they prove to be miracle cures, will do nothing at all to stem the epidemic in poor countries. And who could justify spending anything on AIDS when a simple filter made from five thicknesses of cheap Bangladeshi sari can save lives by straining out the minute crustacea that carry cholera? The cost-effective solutions to disease are never the cures, they are always the preventions. The money spent on AIDS in the West could have done wonders if spent on preventing malaria, cholera and tuberculosis.

However, even from this I take some comfort. The great majority of deaths in the world are caused not by new, incurable diseases but by old, preventable ones like tuberculosis, dysentery and malaria. Preventing them, and driving down death rates, is a terribly challenging task. It will require money, political effort, economic reform and courage. But it is not impossible that things will get better. It is mere defeatism to reject the possibility. The promise of DNA vaccines, in particular, is remarkable. If they live up to expectations they will provide effective, safe vaccines for all sorts of diseases at a cost that even poor countries can afford and in a form that can be distributed by even the exiguous infrastructure of a poor, tropical country. The chances are high that the third millennium will not be punctuated, as the second was, by terrible plagues.

Further Reading

Bray, R. S., *Armies of Pestilence* (Lutterworth, Cambridge, 1997).

Ewald, Paul, *Evolution of Infectious Disease* (Oxford University Press, New York, 1994).

Garrett, Laurie, *The Coming Plague: Newly Emerging Diseases in a World Out of Balance* (Penguin, Harmondsworth, 1994).

Institute of Medicine, *Emerging Infections* (National Academy Press, Washington, DC, 1992).

Karlen, Arno, *Plague's Progress* (Victor Gollancz, London, 1997).

McCormick, Joseph B. and Fisher-Hoch, Susan, *The Virus Hunters* (Bloomsbury, London, 1996).

McNeill, William, *Plagues and Peoples* (Doubleday, New York, 1976).

Nesse, Randolph and Williams, George, *Evolution and Healing* (Phoenix, London, 1996).

Preston, Richard, *The Hot Zone* (Random House, New York, 1994).

Ryan, Frank, *Virus X: Understanding the Real Threat of the New Pandemic Plagues* (HarperCollins, London, 1996).

Wills, Christopher, *Plagues: Their Origin, History and Future* (HarperCollins, London, 1996).

Zinsser, Hans, *Rats, Lice and History* (Little Brown, New York, 1934).

PREDICTIONS